CW00864382

ADA,
THE CHICKEN THAT CHANGED

ADA,
THE CHICKEN THAT CHANGED

A True Story

By

Peter Jones

Illustrations by Inge van der Ham

Published by J & J Publishing

First published in Scotland in 2021
by J & J Publishing
Ty Crwn, East Grange, Kinloss, Forres, Moray, IV36 2UD
01343 850 123

Typeset by J & J Publishing
Illustrations Copyright 2021 © Inge van der Ham

ISBN: 978-0-9543891-2-3

Dedicated to chicken lovers
everywhere and to all those who
celebrate diversity

Cissie and Ada were two rather grandly feathered hens.

They were a pure breed called Bluebells, big, bouncy chickens
with a fabulous grey-blue plumage that they fussed over
to keep it just so and looking their best.

Their owners, Peter and Jacqui, gave them the names
because they reminded them of characters from an
old TV comedy show.

Cissie and Ada arrived at their new home in Scotland
during early spring as young hens that were
about to start laying eggs.

These are called point-of-lay hens because they're just about
ready to start their egg-laying career.

It was a house with a large garden, a big run and lots
of different things to do and eat.

Peter and Jacqui had kept chickens for many years to
provide them and their family
with lovely fresh eggs.

Cissie and Ada agreed they'd done well to land here, and
life will be easy so long as
they each laid a few
eggs a week.

Cissie and Ada were introduced to the others in the coop - the chicken's house – which contained just a couple of brown hybrid hens called Nippy and Sweetie.

Hybrid hens are bred to lay as many eggs as possible, and just had plain brown plumage.

They were called Nippy and Sweetie, a Scottish nickname for someone who can be annoying just by talking. Both Nippy and Sweetie could be really annoying, always clucking very loudly just because they had laid an egg.

But as far as Cissie and Ada were concerned these hybrids were not as posh as them.

They agreed to get along but wouldn't mix socially, and that if Cissie or Ada needed the nest box to lay an egg they would get priority. This shows how dumb chickens can be, which isn't surprising as their brains are the size of two small peanuts.

Soon after they arrived Cissie and Ada started laying eggs,
and although small at the start they soon
became bigger. Their big, beautiful brown
eggs soon outshone the other eggs
in the nest box laid by
Nippy and Sweetie.

The summer came and everyone in the coop got on OK,
although they all stuck to their agreement
about socialising.

Cissie and Ada enjoyed the scraps of food that were put in the coop as well as scratching about in the garden.

At the end of the summer, as everyone's egg-laying reduced with the shorter days, Ada started to feel a little different.

It was a strange different too. When she saw her reflection in the greenhouse glass, she noticed she'd started growing longer red things – called wattles – from under her chin. She also noticed the red comb on the top of her head – called a 'cockscomb' – was getting bigger, and her chest was puffed out more these days.

She felt differently towards the other hens too – a bit more protective, sometimes bossier but also more caring. It was confusing because she felt she wasn't one of the hen flock anymore.

Still, there was a winter to get through, and egg
production was at a lull.

Hens don't lay many eggs in the winter so their bodies can have
a rest and be ready for the spring when they get
back into laying an egg almost every day.

Maybe it was that. Winter in the north of Scotland can drag on a
bit, and it's only in April that the light becomes good enough
to encourage hens to start laying more eggs. She hoped that
getting back into egg production would help her
return to feeling how she always did.

But that didn't happen to Ada. When April and May came
Cissie, Nippy and Sweetie were each getting into a
five-eggs-a-week routine; but Ada couldn't
produce one solitary egg. It made her feel
sad and, well, different.
Separate.

She was getting worried. Hens that don't lay eggs tend not to be around for long. What was happening?

Then early one morning, as the sun was rising over the Scottish Cairngorm mountains and beamed into their coop on the Moray coast, it happened.

She crowed. Crowed like a cockerel. Not as powerful, or as musical (if you like that sort of thing so early in the day), but a crow, nonetheless.

"What?" she thought. "Hens don't crow! I don't crow!"

But Ada kept crowing all morning, unable to stop until the sun was high in the sky and hens were pecking at their feed. Then she stopped and got on with eating too.

Ada knew then she was changing. She wasn't in control of it, but she knew things were changing inside her, and in her head. None of the other hens took any notice.

After all, Ada was still a chicken like them, she just didn't lay eggs anymore. So what? She still strutted around the place like she owned it. She still scoffed more food than the others. She just didn't lay eggs.

Lucky for Ada, the other hens didn't care. As far as they were concerned everything was pretty much the same. Apart from the crowing thing, which was really annoying. Especially in the summer when it started at 4 o'clock in the morning.

Peter and Jacqui heard the crowing. "But we don't have a cockerel", they said. "Has a stray cockerel entered our garden?"

They checked. No extra chickens. It was a mystery. Then one morning they heard and saw Ada crowing away at the crack of dawn. How is that possible?

They had noticed egg production was down but just thought one of the hens was not pulling their weight. Anyway, how can a hen do what a cockerel does and crow like that?

They checked. They asked the vet. And yes. Very, very rarely a hen will develop cockerel habits, stop laying eggs and crow for all they are worth.

"Ada has to go into the pot for supper as she's not laying eggs anymore", said Peter to Jacqui.

"But she looks so happy in the garden and we love seeing her," said Jacqui. "Couldn't we just let Ada stay? The other hens don't seem to mind her as a cockerel, and she and Cissie look so beautiful in the garden."

It was true that Peter and Jacqui still had plenty of eggs and yes, Cissie and Ada were a handsome pair of chickens that were lovely to see strutting and scratching around the garden.

"So, we're just keeping her as a pet?" asked Peter.
"Why not? We have Oscar the cat and he doesn't lay eggs, but we like to have him with us," said Jacqui.
He had to agree.

So, Ada stayed. And the other hens treated her the same as ever, even though she never laid another egg. Ada was glad the others still treated her the same as ever, and that her and Cissie were still the best of friends.

11

But one day, after another morning's crowing, Ada knew her name didn't fit any more. She had changed so much that something else had to change too. Her name.

She had become more like a 'him' than a 'her'. He decided he wanted to be called Adam rather than Ada and called the other hens together to announce his new name.

They all understood and agreed to call him Adam from now on.

But really nothing changed for the chickens.

Everyone still got on in the same way.

Adam was still a chicken, but one that looked, sounded and behaved like a cockerel. That actually didn't matter to the other hens – he was still the fussy, snobby and very smart Bluebell chicken they all knew; he just didn't lay eggs like they did.

And when he crowed in the morning, all the hens rolled their eyes and said: "There he goes, waking everyone up again". But secretly they were comforted by his crowing. Cissie was particularly happy knowing that her friend was with her, and although he couldn't father any chicks and didn't lay eggs, no-one minded.

It was good he was still around.

They liked him for that just as they always did.

This is the true story of a chicken called Ada who changed from a female hen to a male cockerel and thought she would lose her hen friends as a result.

On average, one in every 10,000 hens naturally develop male characteristics during their lifetime. Cockerels do not change to hens.

These rare hens do not completely change into a cockerel; the transition is limited to making the chicken crow, grow larger cockerel-like combs and wattles on their heads and it generally stops laying eggs.

The changed chicken cannot fertilise another hen or carry out other functions of a true male bird. It does not attempt to mate with a hen. However, it can fulfil other functions of a protective male chicken (cockerel) in a group of hens, such as sourcing food, alerting to danger (by emitting a particular squawk), and generally corralling them into groups.

And crowing. Loudly and early!

Printed in Great Britain
by Amazon